Thirteen Candles

Mary Hooper

Illustrated by Maureen Gray

A & C Black · London

GRAFFIX

Roller Madonnas · Bernard Ashley
Roy Kane TV Detective · Steve Bowkett
Bodyparts · Theresa Breslin
Moving the Goalposts · Rob Childs
Captain Hawk · Jim Eldridge
Laser Quest · Mick Gowar
Matthew's Goals · Michael Hardcastle
Thirteen Candles · Mary Hooper
The Headless Ghost · Pete Johnson
The Listener · Elizabeth Laird
A Boy Like That · Tony Langham
Biker · Anthony Masters
Otherworld · Jeremy Strong
Lovesick · Lynda Waterhouse

First paperback edition 1999
First published 1998 in hardback by
A & C Black (Publishers) Ltd
35 Bedford Row, London WC1R 4JH

Text copyright © 1998 Mary Hooper
Illustrations copyright © 1998 Maureen Gray
Cover illustration copyright © 1998 Mike Adams

ISBN 0-7136-4984-4

A CIP catalogue for this book is available from
the British Library.

Printed and bound in Spain by G. Z. Printek, Bilbao.

Chapter One

My thirteenth birthday: 23rd July. It was a hot, happy day. There were balloons and 'Happy Birthday, Julia!' streamers over the wall in the dining room and I was with my mum, dad and best friend Emma.

A CD player! Great! Thanks, Dad!

Mum had some soppy idea about having a proper sit-down birthday party, but apart from that everything was perfect.

Now, isn't this lovely! Just like when you were three.

For goodness sake, Mum!

Well, I miss all that. I liked it when you were into balloons rather than boys...

As I said, it was a perfect day. So why was there a funny knot in my tummy? Why was there a strange shivery tingle going up and down my spine?

I'd tried my best to ignore it, but it wouldn't go away. In the afternoon - well, something really strange happened.

Okay, Jules, brace yourself. Here comes the cake!

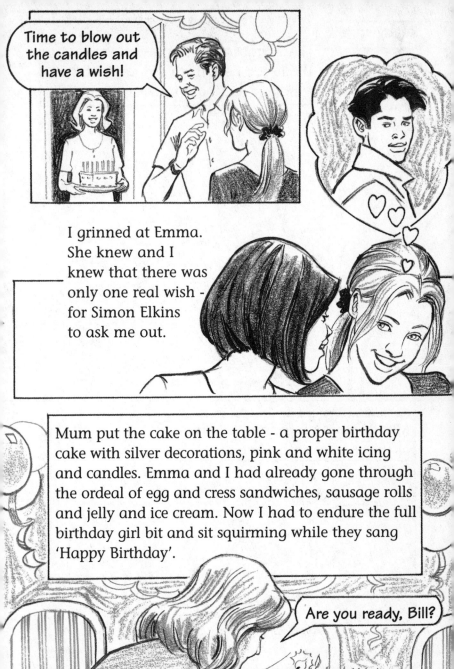

Time to blow out the candles and have a wish!

I grinned at Emma. She knew and I knew that there was only one real wish - for Simon Elkins to ask me out.

Mum put the cake on the table - a proper birthday cake with silver decorations, pink and white icing and candles. Emma and I had already gone through the ordeal of egg and cress sandwiches, sausage rolls and jelly and ice cream. Now I had to endure the full birthday girl bit and sit squirming while they sang 'Happy Birthday'.

Are you ready, Bill?

8

The heat from the candles was making my cheeks warm. 'Okay,' I thought, 'birthday cakes are for kids - but if I'm having a cake, then I might as well have the wish that goes with it.' I sorted out my wish in my mind, took a deep breath and pursed my lips in readiness...

Suddenly, right in front of my eyes, the flames on the candles went out. Every last one of them. But I hadn't blown them.

Jolly good! All **together** now...

As Mum, Dad and Emma went into 'Happy Birthday to You' I stared, stunned, at the candles.

Perhaps they were magic ones, a special sort that all went out together. It would be typical of my family to buy trick candles.

But I knew they weren't. Mum had used some out of the same packet for Dad's birthday earlier this year, I'd bought them myself. Then how?

I frowned. How had it happened? A sudden gust of wind? No. It was a stuffy, airless day without a trace of a breeze.

What, then? Had Emma blown them out for me, as a joke? Not that either. The candles streamed their little blue-orange flames away from me before they went out...

The tingle ran right down my spine again and I shivered.

Mum reached for the cake to begin cutting it.

What's up, love? Someone walk over your grave?

Later, Dad filmed me and Emma getting ready to go out, adding some embarrassing commentary.

Here's my gorgeous daughter and her lovely friend getting ready to hit the town's high-spots!

Oh Dad, turn that thing off!

Finally, Emma and I managed to escape. We went to hang out for a bit at Centre Point, our local leisure centre, just in case there was anyone there worth chatting to.

The film started in the morning with 'Here's the birthday girl emerging from her duvet!'...

Oh, Dad!

...and carried on through the 'highlights' of the day.

Oh, Dad, not again!

There wasn't. It seemed that anyone really interesting (by that I meant Simon Elkins or Richard James), had gone away for the weekend. So, it didn't look as if I was going to get my birthday wish - not today, at any rate.

Just our luck. What shall we do now?

Let's go and see what's going on in the hall. Maybe there will be someone just as good looking as Simon or Richard!

We had a coke, and then sat and watched some boys who were playing basketball.

Nice basket! Shame about the legs!

Not exactly the Harlem Globetrotters, are you?

Think you can do better? Come and give it a try!

And then we walked home. Not the most thrilling birthday in the world.

When we got back, Dad and Mum were waiting to watch the playback of the video.

Take your seats in the front stalls! Ice creams will be served in the interval.

Dads!

Emma and I pulled faces at each other; my one consolation was that her dad's nearly as bad as mine. We sat on the floor, lolling one each side of a squashy cushion, while Dad slid the video into the machine.

It was all pretty boring stuff until we got to the bit with the cake and the candles. Then it stopped being boring and got puzzling - and weird and mysterious and scary as well.

I watched myself looking sheepishly at the camera, saw my intake of breath, saw my mouth pucker - and then I saw a shadow behind me, a dark, hazy shape, leaning forward, over my shoulder.

The film finished with a handwritten card saying:

AND SO ENDS JULIA'S THIRTEENTH BIRTHDAY CELEBRATION!

I couldn't wait to escape. As soon as I could, I dragged Emma up to my room.

Did you see it?

Did you see that shady thing behind me?

Emma nodded.

What d'you think it was?

I don't know. A fault on the film or something, I expect.

I shook my head.

No!
It was something else.
Something real.
It blew the candles out!

Emma looked round at me, eyes wide.

What d'you mean?

Just what I said.
I didn't blow those candles out.
It did.

You're crazy. What are you trying to say - that it was a ghost or something?

I nodded, suddenly really scared, and shivered as an icy tingle went down my spine.

That's just what I do mean. A ghost.

Chapter Two

I didn't sleep well that night. That's unusual for me - I normally crash out as soon as I close my eyes and don't budge until morning.

Instead I kept having this dream - or nightmare - in which I was being followed by a shadow which disappeared every time I turned round to face it.

Several times I woke up and looked fearfully into the corners of my room, searching for shadows...

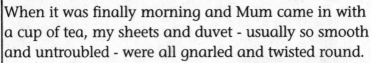

When it was finally morning and Mum came in with a cup of tea, my sheets and duvet - usually so smooth and untroubled - were all gnarled and twisted round.

Are you all right? It looks as if you've been having a fight with someone!

I got dressed and went downstairs to have breakfast. While I was chomping on my cornflakes, I glanced at Mum's magazine. It was open at the astrology page.

Hmm. Let's see what the stars have in store for me...

29

I stopped with a spoonful of cornflakes halfway to my mouth.

I'd felt weird and apprehensive all day yesterday, then those spooky things had happened, and then there had been the nightmares. Together, they foretold something dreadful...

I put down the spoon and turned the magazine round so I could read the whole piece.

LEO 22 July-22 August
If your birthday is the 23rd July, you're in danger of getting everything you want.

I breathed again, then stuffed in another mouthful of cornflakes.

'Julia Parsons,' I thought to myself, 'you're getting daft in your old age.'

You're looking for trouble where there's none. Those things - the candles and the shadow on the film - well, they'd been just a draught of wind and a trick of the light.

31

Emma came over later and we decided to go into town and do some shopping. Pretty soon we were having a laugh about the goings-on of the day before.

Your mum is something else!

Tell me about it!

Dainty triangle sandwiches indeed - she thinks she's at the Ritz!

Emma grinned and nudged me.

Here - what's it worth not to tell Simon
what sort of a party you had?

You dare!

I'd almost forgotten the things that had happened -
except that the words 'You're in danger' would
persist in repeating themselves over and over in
rhythm with my footsteps as we walked along.
I didn't say anything to Emma, though, I knew
she'd just think I was being silly.

When we got home, Dad was filming again. He'd borrowed next door's dog and he was in the front garden with it, trying to make it do tricks. I think he was hoping it would do something really silly and then he could send the film in to the TV and get some money.

When Emma and I turned up, he made us play-act this daft scene for him.

It's just a bit of fun. I want you to take Rover here for a walk, and I'll film you going up the road.

Then what?

We duly walked up the road with Rover between us.

Per-lease, when's the novelty going to wear off? He's like a kid with that camcorder!

Sorry. It was canoes last year. And then mountain bikes the year before that. It could be worse, though.

Yeah, we could all be bungee jumping.

Once Mr Film Producer of the Year had finished, we went round to Emma's house for something to eat. When we got back to mine, Dad wanted us to sit down and watch the film he'd made.

Roll up! Roll up! I think you're going to like this.

Dutifully, we went into the sitting room and took our seats in front of the TV.

When it came to the bit where I was walking down the road with Emma, I just couldn't believe what I saw.

It's there again, behind me! Look! The shadow!

It's only your dad's technique. Of course it's bound to be a bit shaky and out of focus while he's learning.

Do you mind! I'm a professional!

Emma nodded slowly, staring at the screen.

41

Emma leaned closer to the screen to get a better look.

No, it's not. It's like you've got someone standing behind you. Your double.

Just as she said that two things happened: the film came to an end and Mum dropped the cup of tea she was holding.

We all looked at each other, and then Mum dashed out of the room looking as if she was going to burst into tears.

What was that all about?

Dad was all of a fluster.

Your mum's just upset because... because that's her best cup she's broken.

I looked at Dad hard. It couldn't have been that, because it was a really old cup, not her best china at all. No, something else had upset her. And it was something to do with that shadow...

Chapter Three

There was definitely something up. Since my birthday, my life had subtly changed. Mum seemed different, quieter and preoccupied. Several times I caught her staring into space and looking wistful.

44

I knew I wasn't imagining things, though. The shivery, half-frightened feeling that had started on my birthday stayed with me, and often at night I'd lay awake with the words, 'You're in danger' pounding through my head.

Once, just as the downstairs clock was striking three, I woke suddenly and sat up in bed, certain that there was someone in the room - certain Shadow was there.

Who's there?

What d'you want?

I stared towards the window, where a street light shone dimly through my blind. A shape was outlined there: a blurry mass silhouetted against the light.

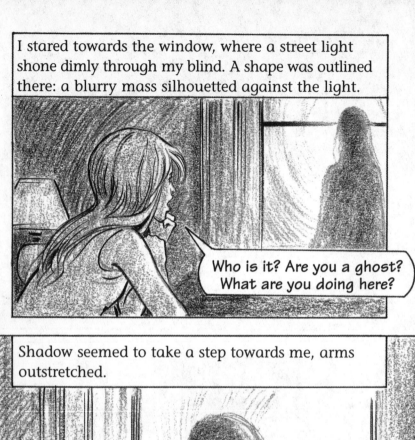

Who is it? Are you a ghost? What are you doing here?

Shadow seemed to take a step towards me, arms outstretched.

I choked back a cry of fright and automatically put out my hand to turn on my bedside light. As I did, Shadow disappeared, leaving me wondering whether I'd just dreamed it.

I couldn't go back to sleep after that; I left the light on and read until it was light.

I began to want to get away from the house. A couple of nights I stayed over at Emma's and I found it much easier to sleep there.

I started looking forward to going away on holiday. Our proper holiday wasn't going to be until the end of September, though, which seemed years away.

So I was pleased when Dad said we were going to stay in a caravan at the seaside for a long weekend.

Can Emma come too?

Sure, why not?

I wasn't so pleased when we got there and it rained for two days. Emma and I just sat around watching the rain running down the windows.

If this raindrop gets to the bottom first, then Simon's going to ask me out before we go back to school.

No. If this raindrop gets there first, then Richard's going to ask me.

Only once I brought up the subject of Shadow, but Emma didn't seem to want to talk about it.

You remember that strange thing that happened on my birthday...

The only strange thing that happened on your birthday was being made to sit down and eat jelly and ice cream!

On the day we were going home the wind stopped and the sun came out.

Dad's camcorder put in an appearance, too.

Okay, girls - the sun's shining. Let's have some volley-ball on the beach!

He packed the camcorder into a bag and headed for the door.

I'll be getting out of practice with this if I'm not careful.

Emma and I put on our shorts and compared legs to see who was brownest.

I am! My legs are olive brown.

Well, mine are freckly golden brown.

YEAH?

That's just as brown - but in a different way.

Not so dark, though.

Bet you used fake tan before we came away.

Ooh, I did not!

We made our way down the cliff steps to where Mum and Dad had set up camp on the sand.

At last!

Hurry up, you two!

Coming, Mum.

Dad had made a makeshift volley-ball net from a windbreak.

Okay, you two, here's the ball.

He positioned himself on some rocks and shouted at us to begin.

Okay, I want lots of action!

Give us a chance to warm up, first.

I only want to be filmed from my best side!

You haven't got a best side!

53

I ran over to get it back. The cliffs had cast large shadows on the beach and, as I went into the shade, the sand was suddenly cold under my feet. Without the warmth of the sun, I shivered, half from cold and half from, well, that feeling again. That frightened, scary feeling that someone was close to me, all the time watching me.

I paused for a moment. 'You're crazy,' I told myself. 'Don't be such a drip!'

I took a step towards the ball - and then I heard a strange rumbling coming from above me.

I stayed frozen to the spot and suddenly I felt - and saw - Shadow.

It seemed to come towards me from out of the cliff, growing deeper and denser as it did so.

You're in danger!

I wanted to scream but there wasn't time. Shadow just literally shoved me off my feet, throwing me sideways so that I landed in a heap on the sand.

I heard Emma and Dad shout something - and then there was an almighty crashing noise and I automatically curled up and felt myself being hit by a shower of small stones.

CRAASH

When I opened my eyes, Dad, Mum and Emma were all racing towards me.

Are you all right?

Oh, Julia!

It was a moment before I realised what had happened: a chunk of the cliff face had fallen exactly where I'd been standing - I could see a piece of the beach ball there to prove it. If Shadow hadn't shoved me out of the way, I'd have been killed...

Chapter Four

That beach ball, it was squashed flat. That would have been you.

It must have been all the rain. It loosened the structure of the cliff above, somehow...

Mum said nothing, just hugged me.

Sun or no sun, none of us could exactly relax and enjoy the day now. Dad phoned the police, and went to see the coastguard, and then we just drove straight home.

During the journey I thought things over. I didn't know what to think. Had I just dreamed up Shadow? If I had, it was a lucky dream - one which had saved my life. Maybe Dad's video would give me an answer.

61

Never mind.
I'd just like to see
up to then.

Dad thought about it for a
moment, then shrugged.
He popped the cassette
into the machine and
switched it on.

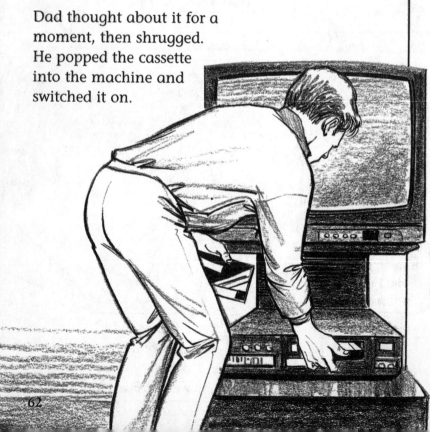

The film began with Emma and me coming down the cliff steps towards Mum and Dad on the beach.

It went blank for a second, then started again with us playing with the ball, knocking it backwards and forwards over the windbreak and calling to each other.

Then Emma punched the ball towards the cliff and it
went out of shot.

I watched myself run off to fetch
it. Reaching the shade I hesitated
for a moment.

Then there was a rumbling noise as,
far above me, the rocks began to fall.

A split second after this we all gasped, and
watched in disbelief as the distinct shape of
a person appeared out of nowhere, arms
stretched out to push me out of danger.

And then it all went blurred and then blacked out
because Dad had stopped filming.

Mum and Dad just sat there in complete silence, looking at each other, then Mum started crying.

Don't cry, love.

I was completely bewildered. Okay, so I'd nearly had a nasty accident, but I was all right now. So why were they both looking at each other in that peculiar way? Why was Mum crying? Then Dad spoke.

You'd better tell her.

Tell me what?

Joy and Julia.
You were like two
peas in a pod.

I gazed at them disbelievingly.
Emma spoke for me.

What happened?

Joy died.
She only lived for a day.

We were so upset, we couldn't bear it to be spoken about. We pretended to most people that there had only been the one baby.

I took a deep breath, and I thought about how strange and how incredible it would have been to have had a twin.

So now...

So now - well, I never would have believed it if I hadn't seen it.

73

But now... perhaps Joy wants to make her presence felt.

The realisation flooded through me.

Of course! She didn't like being forgotten. She wants to be part of the family!

Do you think so?

Yes!

Chapter Five

When I went to bed that night, Mum came in for a chat.

I'm sorry we didn't tell you years ago. I just couldn't bear to speak about it.

That's okay, Mum. I know now.